THE TRAVELS OF MAGNUS POLE

written and illustrated by

Jonathan Wills

CHATTO & WINDUS · LONDON / CANONGATE · EDINBURGH

MAGNUS POLE lived a long time ago on the island of Yell, in Shetland. Yell was, and still is, a hilly sort of place, covered with big brown peat bogs, although round the seashore there are patches of green and small farms. Magnus Pole had a very small farm with hardly enough land to grow food for his family. Like all the farmers in Yell he kept a boat on the beach below his farm.

The weather in Yell was usually windy and wet, so very often the crops would get blown flat and go rotten before Magnus Pole managed to bring in the harvest. Every grain of oats and barley had to be ground before it could be made into bread or porage. The grains had to be crushed every day with a knocking stone in a hollow rock. Magnus Pole hated this job more than anything.

What Magnus Pole liked best was fishing. When he grew tired of working the knocking stone he would gather up his fishing-lines and launch his boat for a fishing trip. Sometimes he sailed out so far that he could not hear the shouts of his wife and children. They wanted him to come home and grind up more barley to make bannocks. They were tired of having to spread butter on dried fish, pretending it was bread. One day Magnus Pole was so happy and busy fishing that he sailed too far from the shore. He did not notice that the weather was changing.

A great storm blew up and drove Magnus Pole away from the island, out into the open sea. The wind was so strong that he could not sail against it. Then the sea carried off his oars so he could not row either. For two whole days and nights the storm raged around the tiny boat. All Magnus Pole could do was sit tight and wish that he was back at the knocking stone.

On the third day, just as the sun was rising, the wind suddenly died away. Ahead of him Magnus Pole could see a dark shore and high mountains. It was much too big to be Yell. He had been blown more than two hundred miles to the coast of Norway. He had eaten all the fish he had caught on his first day at sea and he was hungry, tired, and very wet.

A kindly farmer and his wife saw Magnus Pole coming into the fjord and they hurried to give him food and warm clothes. The farmer, who spoke a language very like that of the people of Yell, said it was too late in the year to take him home, because they had already pulled their boat out of the water for the winter. He said that Magnus Pole was welcome to stay with them if he would help on the farm, and in the spring they would take him back to Yell. So they spent the long winter nights feasting, drinking, dancing and telling stories. Magnus Pole thought they had much more to eat and drink in Norway than they did back in Yell.

One fine spring morning, Magnus Pole and his friends set off in a newly painted longship, towing Magnus Pole's own little boat behind them. All the local people came out to see them off. After sailing some way westwards they saw a big Swedish ship coming very fast over the horizon. As she came closer the Norwegians shouted some very rude things at the crew and there was a short but terrible battle. Before Magnus Pole knew what was happening he found himself tied up with his friends as a prisoner. The Norwegian longship was set on fire, and after a while she sank, taking Magnus Pole's own boat with her to the bottom of the ocean.

TOR
TOR

The Swedes took their prisoners back to the King of Norway and made him pay a ransom before setting them free. But when it came to Magnus Pole's turn, of course the King had never heard of him, so he had to join up with the Swedish crew who were on their way to sell whale oil and salted fish to their cousins in Russia. For many days they sailed across the Baltic Sea. It was foggy and cold. Magnus Pole shivered a lot and felt very sad as they sailed further and further away from Yell. Then at last they saw a long, low coast, with muddy creeks and great forests of fir trees. They left the sea behind them and sailed up a big river through the forest.

Magnus Pole had never seen forests before. There were no trees at all in Yell, but here in Russia the people even built their houses of wood and burned great logs in their fires day and night. These strange sights cheered Magnus Pole a little. Then one day the river became so narrow and shallow that there was no room to sail further upstream. So Magnus Pole and the crew cut down trees to make rollers. They laid out the logs in a long line and rolled the ship over them. In this way they crossed the great marshes at the head of the river, and it was a week before they came to another river on which they could launch their ship again. Magnus Pole could not understand how a river could run away from the sea.

For many weeks they sailed down the great river. Now instead of forests there were hundreds of miles of grassland and the tribes who lived by the river-bank were very unfriendly. Every time the ship stopped for the night it was attacked from both sides with bows and arrows. Magnus Pole was beginning to think the river would never end when suddenly it widened so much that both banks disappeared. The air became very hot and dry and the water turned warm and salty. They had reached the Caspian Sea.

It took a long time to cross the Caspian Sea because there was very little wind and it was too hot to row for long. When they got to the other side they unloaded their cargo and sat in the shade to wait for the traders from the east. Magnus Pole went for a swim while they waited. The sea around Yell was too cold for swimming but here the water was warm, and so salty that he could float without trying at all. After a day or two the traders arrived, riding on strange animals called camels. They brought silk, gold and ivory to trade for the furs, honey and tar that the Swedes had bought in Russia. Then the Swedes told Magnus Pole that he could go back to Sweden with them if he liked, or he could go on to China with the traders and their camels. Magnus Pole thought that it would be fun to ride a camel and interesting to see China, so he set off with the traders from the east.

They took nearly two weeks to cross the great desert of Pesky Karakumy to the east of the Caspian Sea. Magnus Pole felt very seasick swaying about on top of his camel and very thirsty, too. He could not understand a word the traders said. At first he wished he had gone back to Sweden, but after a while he began to like the desert, especially when they were amongst the dusty foothills of a mountain range. They crossed through the mountains at a place called the Khyber Pass. Magnus Pole thought he had never seen such beautiful colours. It was even more beautiful than the brown cliffs of Yell.

They crossed another desert, even hotter and drier than the Pesky Karakumy but not quite so big. When they reached the other side they sold the camels and bought horses to carry them on the road to China. Looking ahead and upwards Magnus Pole could see the snowy peaks of the Hindu Kush mountains, the highest in the world. They climbed from the hot desert through warm forests, on to high freezing slopes, and Magnus Pole began to wish that the temperature would stay the same for a while. When they got to a high windy place in Tibet Magnus Pole met a farmer who spoke to him in sign language and offered him a job on his farm. Magnus Pole decided he had done enough travelling for the moment, so he said goodbye to the eastern traders who went their way up into the mountains towards China.

By now winter was coming on again. It snowed a lot and Magnus Pole sat indoors making tools for the farm and clothes for the farmer's family. In spring the snow melted and all the streams were rushing down the slopes full of new snow water. One day the farmer took Magnus Pole down the valley to show him a machine he had built – to make the stream water do the work of milling for him. The stream pushed round a paddle-wheel. The paddle-wheel turned a stone wheel that rested on another flat stone. The stones ground up all the grains of corn which the farmer poured into a hole at the top. This was much better than a knocking stone because the stream water did all the work for him. Magnus Pole felt very excited – it was just what his family wanted!

That day Magnus Pole had a clever idea. If he made a watermill for himself and took it back to Yell, then he need never use his knocking stone again. So he and the Tibetan farmer started work on the mill. Magnus Pole made the log cabin and the farmer made the complicated bits like the waterwheel and the millstones. Then they cut down some trees to make a raft, lifted the new watermill on to it and Magnus Pole set off. He steered his raft down the stream, which joined the River Indus. He followed the Indus for many days until the river left the mountains and spread out over a wide plain. At last the water turned muddy and then salty. He knew he had reached the sea again.

Magnus Pole sat on his raft at the mouth of the river, drifting all over the place and wondering what to do next. Suddenly a fast, sleek sailing ship came into sight. The Captain of this ship came from Arabia and was on his way home from a trip to India to buy spices. He was astonished to find Magnus Pole sitting on a strange raft with a watermill on it. Magnus Pole pointed to the west and the captain nodded. He was going that way too. The crew hauled the watermill on to the ship and Magnus Pole travelled with them along the coast of Arabia and up the Red Sea.

When they reached the northern end of the Red Sea they tied up at the shore and began to unload the watermill. But as the crew was lowering it over the side a rope broke and the mill crashed to the ground, breaking into a hundred pieces. Magnus Pole was so upset that the Captain tried to help him mend the watermill, but it was no use. So he gave him some gold coins and a camel to take him through a small desert to the shores of another sea, the Mediterranean. There he would find a ship to take him home to Yell. Magnus Pole thanked him and set off once more. He carried with him the most important bits of the watermill, the grinding stones and the paddle-wheel.

On the shores of the sea with the long name Magnus Pole saw a sight that made him jump and dance for joy. It was a Norwegian trading ship and the men had horns on their helmets just like his. He ran towards them as fast as his legs would carry him. Even the camel had a job to keep up. The Norwegians had heard of Magnus Pole's disappearance into the east and told him that everyone in Yell had given him up for lost. What a party they had that night to celebrate Magnus Pole's return! It was spoken about all over Norway for many years to come, and a poet even wrote a poem about it.

Next morning they all had sore heads from drinking too much wine. Late in the afternoon they sailed to the west, following the coast of North Africa and keeping a look-out for pirates. On the way home Magnus Pole tried to explain about the watermill. The Norwegians listened politely, but between themselves they thought that Magnus Pole's travels had turned his brain. They could not see how a watermill worked and they had never heard of Tibet. As they neared the Rock of Gibraltar they ran into a very bad storm. Magnus Pole and the crew were too busy sailing the ship and being seasick to notice when the sea washed the millstones and the paddle-wheel over the side. The stones sank and the wheel drifted away, never to be seen again.

Now Magnus Pole had nothing to show for his wanderings but some gold coins and the idea of the watermill in his head. As he watched the island of Yell coming out of the mist he had a feeling that no one would believe him. Magnus Pole's uncles rowed out in their boat to take him ashore and his wife and children greeted him with joy. The whole island came to Magnus Pole's homecoming feast and everyone was glad to see him safe and well. They enjoyed his stories about where he had been and what he had seen, but they laughed at the one about Tibet and the watermill. Magnus Pole got very angry at this and shouted that he would show them all he was telling the truth.

Magnus Pole and his brothers set to work to make a watermill. This time Magnus Pole made the difficult bits like the paddle-wheel and the millstones, and his brothers made the little mill house from driftwood and beach stones. Some of the people who didn't believe him watched secretly from behind walls and haystacks. Magnus Pole's mill became a great joke on the island. But in a week it was finished. They stopped laughing and came to watch in wonder as Magnus Pole ground more oats and barley in a day than they had ever done in a week.

By the next winter Magnus Pole had made three more watermills and everyone had forgotten their knocking stones. No one ever disbelieved him again. Magnus Pole no longer went fishing at sea to escape from the knocking stone. What he liked much better was to sit by the loch, listening to the clackety-clack of his watermills and fishing for trout, which tasted far nicer than the fish that came from the sea.

And that is why, if you look carefully, you will find the ruins of little watermills along nearly every stream in Yell. To say nothing of Tibet, of course.